Don't Rush Me!

For Siblings of Children with Sensory Processing Disorder (SPD)

by Chynna T. Laird

Loving Healing Press

Ann Arbor

Don't Rush Me! For Siblings of Children with Sensory Processing Disorder (SPD)

From the Growing With Love series

Library of Congress Cataloging-in-Publication Data
Laird, Chynna T., 1970-
Don't rush me! : for siblings of children with sensory processing disorder (SPD) / by Chynna T. Laird.
pages cm. -- (Growing with love)
Audience: Age 5-8.
Audience: K to grade 3.
ISBN 978-1-61599-264-5 (pbk. : alk. paper) -- ISBN 978-1-61599-265-2 (ebook)
1. Sensory integration dysfunction in children--Juvenile literature. 2. Sensory disorders in children--Juvenile literature. I. Title.
RJ496.S44L33 2015
618.92'8--dc23
2014049747

Published by
Loving Healing Press
5145 Pontiac Trail
Ann Arbor, MI 48105

Toll free: 888-761-6268 (USA/CAN)
Fax: 734-663-6861

Distributed by Ingram Book Group (USA/CAN), Bertram's Books (UK/EU)

To: Jordy – Don’t ever change. xo

Everyone in my family moves way... too... fast. They walk fast. They eat fast. They even talk fast. Yep. Everyone is fast around here. Except me. And I know it bugs them.

If I stay in bed too long in the morning, Mama comes into my room, making one of those Mommy frustrated faces. Her cheeks turn red, and she says, "Mia! You're going to be late for school! Please get up right now!"
I just yawn and tell her, "Don't rush me. I like taking my time."

When I am taking too long picking out just the right beautiful outfit—because I like to look beautiful—Daddy knocks on my door and says, "What are you doing, Mia? You've been in here for half an hour picking your clothes. You still have to eat breakfast. Please get moving! We have a lot to do if we are to get everything done and everyone where they have to be!"

He doesn't understand that being beautiful takes time. I tell him, "Don't rush me, Daddy. I like taking my time."

He takes his glasses off, rubs his forehead then shuts the door.

If it takes me a bit longer than everyone else to eat my dinner, my sister Alexandra says, "Oh come on, Mia! None of us can leave until you're done! Just hurry up and eat!"
I chew and swallow what's in my mouth—since that's what proper ladies are supposed to do—and I say to her, "Don't rush me. I like taking my time."
Usually she just glares at me. But I still take my time.

I have a nice walk, I think. Not too fast, not too slow. I like seeing everything around us when we walk to school. And I love saying 'Hi!' or 'Goodbye!' to people I know. But my walk is never fast enough for everyone else. They always say, "Please pick up the pace, Mia! We're going to be late!"
I adjust my beautiful movie star sunglasses and say, "Don't rush me. I like taking my time." Everybody in my family needs something special for them. I need to take my time.
I end up being last in line-up or running to catch up when the bell rings but I'm okay with that.

Sometimes it makes me really sad when people try rushing me. I try to hurry, like they ask, but I just end up making a mess or falling down or something. So I go slower so that stuff doesn't happen. And good stuff happens when I'm slower.

Like I can help Alexandra feel better when stuff around her makes her feel overwhelmed or angry or scared. She doesn't like certain sounds or smells or the way some of her clothes feel. Mama calls that 'sensory overload' and it happens to Alexandra a lot. But I always know what to do when she needs to slow down so she feels safer and calmer, like a bear hug or her favorite squeezy tool.

I can make my little brother, Michael, stop yelling when he's really mad or things around him make him start bumping into people and furniture on purpose because that feels good to him, not because he wants to be annoying. When he's really worked up, his speech gets all garbley gooky, and no one knows what he wants. I can always help him slow down so grown ups understand what he's trying to say. He gets sensory overload too. But his kind is different.

Going slower also means I can see stuff that my baby sister, Laura, drops when no one hears her trying to tell them what she needs. I always find that stuff for her, and make her feel better.

See? Not rushing can be a good thing. And the best part is when Mama sees the stuff I do when I slow down and she gives me a big squeezy bear hug.

“Come on, Mama. Please hurry. I want to go outside and play!”

My Mama smiles with one of those happy, teary Mommy smiles and says, “Don’t rush me. I like taking my time.”

Grown ups. What are you gonna do with them?

You Are an Important Piece in Your Family Puzzle

This is a great book for the whole family to enjoy together. Did you know that each person in your family has an important job in helping things run smoothly each day, just like every part of a car needs to work together to make it go? If one part of a car doesn't work properly or isn't taken care of very well, it isn't going to go. And the same thing is true about a family.

Mia is just like my daughter, Jordhan. They both love their sisters and brothers very much but both of them often feel sad, mad or even a little bit lonely. Mia's siblings, like my Jordhan, have Sensory Processing Disorder and other special needs, which means it can sometimes take a bit of extra work taking care of them. And that means Mia (and Jordhan) don't always feel they get enough attention or special care themselves. That's why Mia moves…so…slow while everyone else around her moves so fast. It's her way of making her own place and showing what she can do. And in slowing down, she sees things that the other people around her don't always have time to see. That's pretty cool!

It's really important that all kids in a family feel good about who they are, what they can do and what they do to help their family as a whole. Because without your help, the family won't run the same—just like the car. Here are a few ways you and your family can make sure everyone gets that extra love and attention. See how many you can try together or, even better, how many you can come up with on your own!

Learn everything you can about your sibling's condition. The more you know about what's going on with your sibling, the more you'll understand him and the bigger help you can be to him and the rest of your family. We have an expression in our house that goes, "Knowledge is a powerful thing!"

Have at least one daily meal together. Sometimes, busy families aren't always able to eat every meal together. But it's a great way to connect, bond and have everyone share thoughts and ideas. In our house, we have dinner together every night. Each of us has our own special place at the table and we take turns talking about what happened during our day. If dinner can't work out, try breakfast!

Have a family game night. You could play board games, video games (like Wii) or just put music on and dance.

Have a 'sharing time'. This is when the whole family gets together to talk about feelings, ideas or problems. Every person in the family needs to know their voice can be heard, their feelings matter, their ideas count and that their problems are a concern too. When each person is allowed to talk about what's on his or her mind—no matter if it's good or bad or somewhere in between—he or she feels like an active member of the family. Each person should have equal talking and listening time.

Me time, We Time and Us Time. In our house, this is our expression for needing to have time with everyone in the family, special one-on-one time with our sibling(s) or Mom and Dad, then time on our own. Each of these times is very important because it helps to make us feel good about living where we do and with the people we live with. And it helps to strengthen things called 'self-esteem' (believing in yourself), 'respect' (treating ourselves and others the way they deserve to be treated) and 'self-worth' (believing you are a good, beautiful person who deserves all the good things in life).

Share lots of hugs, kisses, cuddles and other mushy stuff. Hugs are very important. They feel good to give and to get and they make us feel wanted and loved. Hugging also helps people stay healthier by building up your immune system. Give, and get, as many as you can, especially to the people in your family. It matters!

Have your friends over. You should feel you can have your friends over for playtime fun. Don't worry about what they'll think of your sibling. He might talk differently or act in an unusual way or may not look the same as other kids do but it's okay. Having people see that your sibling is just a regular kid aside from his struggles is called 'acceptance' and that's awesome.

Be sure to go out and have your own fun. You need to get out there and have some fun outside of your house. Go on playdates to your friends' houses, go to the park, enjoy your own activities and never feel guilty about that. Guilt is that feeling you can get in your tummy when you don't feel good about something. You need to get out there and have your own experiences aside from what goes on in your house. That's so important because just like your sibling, you have so much more about you to let people see. So, get out there and let people see those other things!

What Makes You An Important Part of Your Family?

You are a very important part of your family, you know. Let's find out more about what makes you a special piece of your family puzzle.

Everybody has one thing they can do really well. What's your one thing?

____

____

Why do you like doing that thing so much? How does it make you feel?

____

____

'Unique' is a word that means there is nobody else in the world exactly like you. How are you unique?

____

____

____

____

Describe some of the funtime activities you like to do.

____

____

____

____

Who are your friends? What activities do you like doing with your friends?

What makes you happy?

What makes you sad?

What makes you mad?

What do you do when you're feeling sad or mad or jealous? Do you talk to someone? Do you do something fun? Describe it.

What kinds of special things do you do as part of your family?

____

____

____

Draw a picture of you and your family doing your favorite 'Family Time' activity.

Draw a picture of yourself and color it in. Show everything special about you in your picture.

Mia's perfect day would be getting to dress up, have a fashion show, eat frosted cookies and have extra cuddles with Mama. Describe your perfect day. What makes it perfect? Why did you choose those things?

About the Author

CHYNNA LAIRD – is a freelance writer and author living in Edmonton, Alberta with her partner and her four children. Her passion is helping children and families living with Sensory Processing Disorder and other special needs. You'll find her work in many online and in-print parenting, inspirational, Christian and writing publications in Canada, United States, Australia, and Britain. In addition, she's authored an award-winning children's book (*I'm Not Weird, I Have SPD*), two memoirs (the multi award-winning, *Not Just Spirited: A Mom's Sensational Journey With SPD and White Elephants*), a Young Adult novel (*Blackbird Flies*), an adult Suspense/Thriller (*Out of Sync*), and a Young Adult /Paranormal/ Romance (*Dark Water*). She's also working a few other projects in the works for Middle Grade and Young Adult readers.

Please visit Chynna's Website at
http://www.chynnalairdauthor.ca

Also by Chynna T. Laird

Through Understanding Comes Respect and Love

This book was inspired by the author's daughter, Jaimie, who struggles with Sensory Processing Disorder (SPD) every day. It was written to validate Jaimie's feelings and to show her other children feel things the way she does. This book can help children with SPD learn how to explain their disorder to others; help peers understand what children with SPD go through; and also help therapists, teachers and/or counselors learn how to talk about it. Helping others learn about children with special needs brings understanding to them and help to make them seem less... different.

Not Just Spirited is one mother's journey to finding peace for her daughter, Jaimie.

By the time she turned two, Jaimie was so fearful of her world they spent most days inside. What was wrong with Chynna's miracle girl? Why wouldn't anyone help her figure it out? Jaimie wasn't "just spirited" as her physician suggested nor did she lack discipline at home. When Jaimie was diagnosed with Sensory Processing Disorder (SPD) at two-and-a-half, Chynna thought she had "the answer," but that was just the start of a three-year quest for the right treatments to bring the Jaimie she loved so much out for others to see. With the right diagnosis and treatment suited to Jaimie, this family finally felt hope.

Please visit www.LHPress.com/growing-with-love

CPSIA information can be obtained
at www.ICGtesting.com
Printed in the USA
BVHW02s0757090718
521162BV00011B/176/P